FREEDOM TRAIN

Written by
GLEN DOWNEY

Illustrated by
LEIGH DRAGOON

This story is set in the 19th century in the United States. Each chapter ends with a non-fiction page that gives more information about real people's lives and actual events at that time.

OXFORD
UNIVERSITY PRESS

LIZZIE

HARRIET TUBMAN

WILLIAM STILL

MILLARD FILLMORE

MARSHALL DOUGLAS

ELIJAH

MELISSA

REAL PEOPLE IN HISTORY

Harriet Tubman (1822–1913): A runaway slave who helped more than 300 slaves to freedom.

William Still (1821–1902): An author and businessman who helped many slaves to escape. He is often called 'the Father of the Underground Railroad'.

President Millard Fillmore (1800–1874): Although he was against slavery, he signed a law making it illegal for people to help runaway slaves.

FICTIONAL CHARACTERS

Lizzie: A young slave who makes a bid for freedom and the Promised Land.

Marshall Douglas: The son of a slave-owner who makes it his mission to hunt Lizzie down.

Elijah: A man who helps Lizzie escape at a great cost to himself.

Melissa: A young girl who learns something surprising about her family history.

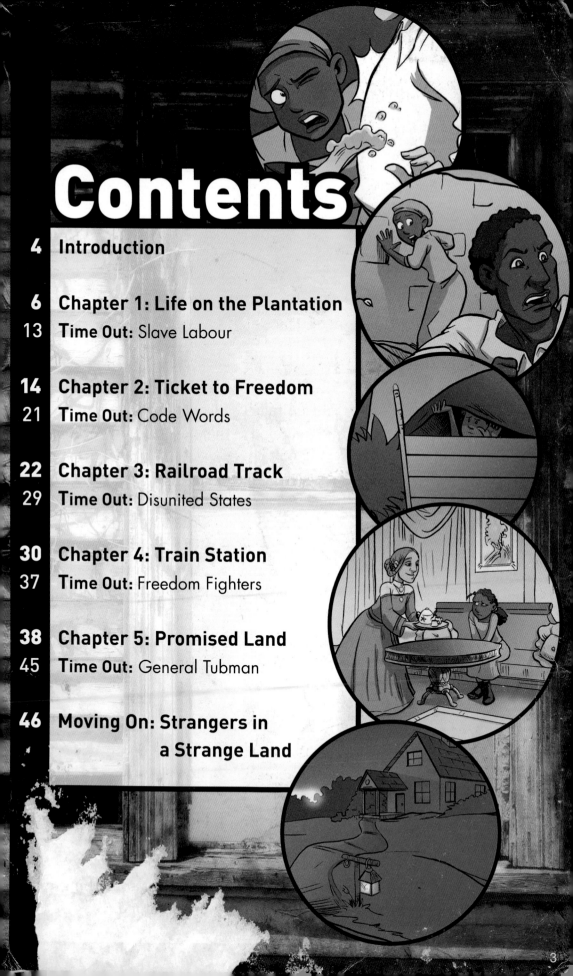

Contents

Fugitive Slave Act cartoon of 1850

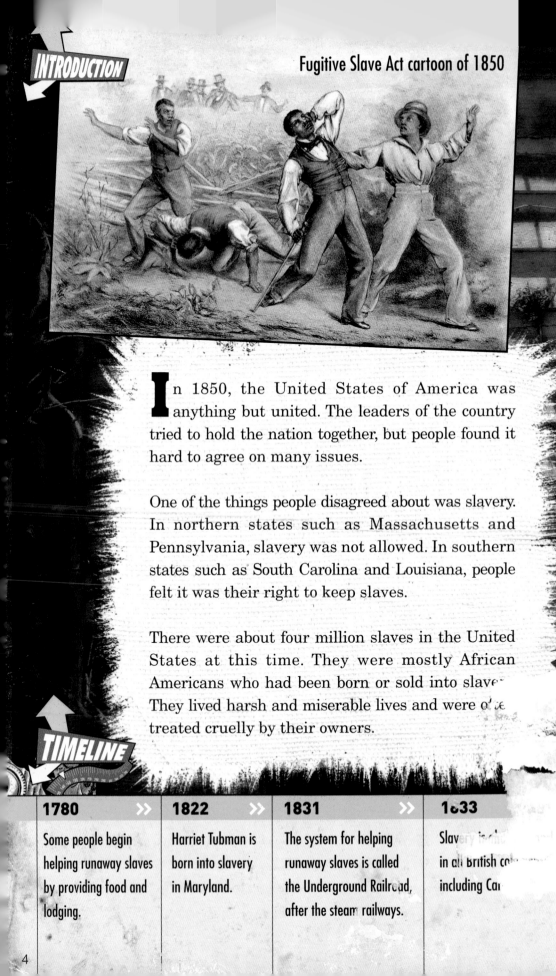

In 1850, the United States of America was anything but united. The leaders of the country tried to hold the nation together, but people found it hard to agree on many issues.

One of the things people disagreed about was slavery. In northern states such as Massachusetts and Pennsylvania, slavery was not allowed. In southern states such as South Carolina and Louisiana, people felt it was their right to keep slaves.

There were about four million slaves in the United States at this time. They were mostly African Americans who had been born or sold into slave They lived harsh and miserable lives and were o' i treated cruelly by their owners.

TIMELINE

1780	1822	1831	1833
Some people begin helping runaway slaves by providing food and lodging.	Harriet Tubman is born into slavery in Maryland.	The system for helping runaway slaves is called the Underground Railroad, after the steam railways.	Slavery in all British co including Ca

Many slaves tried to run away. They headed for a northern state or for Canada, where slavery had been banned for decades. On their way north, these slaves were helped by people who gave them food and shelter. Sometimes they had guides to show them the way. Hundreds of slaves found their way to freedom through this secret network. It became known as the Underground Railroad.

Hunting a runaway slave

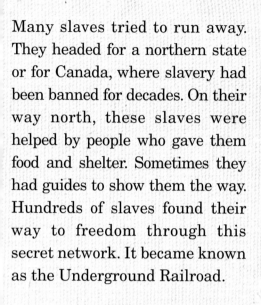

This story is set in an actual time in history, although some of the events are fictional. Real events during this period are shown on the timeline below.

	1850	1856	1861-1865
...rom her ...e free, she helps many others escape.	President Fillmore signs the Fugitive Slave Act, making it illegal for people to help runaway slaves.	The US Supreme Court rules that no black person is a citizen of the United States.	The American Civil War is fought. One of the main reasons is slavery.

Chapter 1: Life on the Plantation

I HAVEN'T FINISHED WITH YOU!
NO!
I'LL SHOW YOU WHAT HAPPENS TO CLUMSY SLAVES.
P...PLEASE, MASTER ...
HELP!
THUD!

SLAVE LABOUR

A scene on a cotton plantation

People in the southern states grew crops such as tobacco and cotton on large plantations. They had slaves to work in the fields.

These slaves had been brought from Africa on slave ships or born into slavery on American shores. They were considered to be property that could be bought and sold like anything else. They were often whipped and beaten, and they were hardly thought of as human beings.

It had not always been this way. In the early 17th century, whites worked beside blacks as equals. All exchanged a few years' hard labour for a chance to own land.

Over time, the system changed, and most African Americans were forced into slavery. In 1776, the Declaration of Independence said US citizens had rights to 'life, liberty and the pursuit of happiness' – but this did not apply to black slaves.

CODE WORDS

The Underground Railroad was a secret system. Anyone who wanted to be a part of it had to learn some secret code words:

> An agent was someone who knew where the railroad operated and could put slaves on the right track.

> A passenger was a runaway slave who used the railroad to escape. Passengers were sometimes called cargo.

> A station was a safe house where the runaway slave could get some food and rest before moving on.

> A stationmaster was the owner of the safe house.

A station had a lantern hanging on the hitching post outside. In those days, people tied their horses to hitching posts.

Agents and runaway slaves, or passengers, introduced themselves with the password 'a friend of a friend'.

DISUNITED STATES

In 1850, President Fillmore made it illegal for people to help runaway slaves, even in states where slavery had been banned. Yet Fillmore was himself opposed to slavery. So why did he do it?

By that time, the northern and southern states did not trust one another. The fight over slavery threatened to tear the country apart. Fillmore was desperate to unite the two sides. He felt that signing the law was a way to find middle ground with the South.

A few years later, Abraham Lincoln declared, 'A house divided against itself cannot stand'. He was right. In 1861, 11 southern states separated from the rest of the union, and the country plunged into civil war.

"NOW THAT LIZZIE HAD ARRIVED AT THE FIRST STATION, SHE FELT VERY UNEASY."

HERE'S A CUP OF TEA, LIZZIE. YOU MUST BE HUNGRY.

NO, MA'AM. THANK YOU, MA'AM.

YOU CAN TRUST ME, LIZZIE. YOU KNOW THAT?

YES, MA'AM.

I SUPPOSE YOU'RE NOT USED TO TRUSTING WHITE FOLKS, ARE YOU?

NO, MA'AM. I GUESS NOT.

TELL MISS HARRIET THAT THIS CARGO IS BOUND FOR THE PROMISED LAND.
YES, SIR.
PLEASE ALSO TELL HER THAT THE WIND BLOWS FROM THE SOUTH TODAY.
WIND BLOWS FROM THE SOUTH TODAY, EH?
MR DOUGLAS WILL BE INTERESTED TO HEAR THAT!

FREEDOM FIGHTERS

There were many people in the North who spoke out against slavery. These three people made a difference:

William Still (1821–1902)

- Born a free black man and became a successful businessman
- Helped 649 slaves to freedom
- Wrote books about the evil of slavery

Harriet Beecher Stowe (1811–1896)

- Wrote *Uncle Tom's Cabin* about the life of slaves
- Spoke about the cruelty of slavery
- Was called 'the little lady who made this big war' by Abraham Lincoln

Frederick Douglass (1818–1895)

- Escaped from slavery when he was 20
- Wrote a book about his life as a slave
- Printed newspapers against slavery

GENERAL TUBMAN

TIME OUT!

Harriet Tubman was the most famous conductor on the Underground Railroad. She made 19 daring trips into the South to free more than 300 slaves. She boasted, "I never ran my train off the track, and I never lost a passenger."

Tubman was a runaway slave herself. Sometimes she fell into a very deep sleep without warning – the result of being hit on the head by her owner.

As if freeing slaves was not enough, Tubman was also a nurse, spy and soldier during the Civil War. She was the first woman in US history to plan and carry out a military raid. For that reason, she was called General Tubman.

Harriet Tubman with a group of former slaves late in her life

STRANGERS IN

Descendants of fugitive slaves in an
Underground Railroad village school, 1909

A number of slaves settled in northern US states, but they were always in danger of being found by their former owners. A better chance for a new life lay even further north.

More than 30,000 slaves escaped to freedom in Canada. Large numbers settled in southern Ontario in cities such as Windsor, St. Catharines and Toronto. Others went as far as Halifax, Nova Scotia and Vancouver Island in British Columbia.

A STRANGE LAND

In Canada, ex-slaves could own land, find work and raise children in freedom. Their former owners no longer had the right to go after them, since slavery had been abolished in Canada in 1833.

Life in the Promised Land was not easy. Black people faced racial prejudice north of the border, too. They were far away from everything they had ever known. As Harriet Tubman said, "I was free, but there was no one to welcome me to the land of freedom. I was a stranger in a strange land."

For many, however, it was the first taste of freedom they had ever had in their lives.

INDEX

GLOSSARY

abolish – to put an end to a law or custom

bill – the draft version of a proposed law to be discussed by Parliament

cargo – goods carried in a ship or aircraft

discouraged – to reduce one's enthusiasm

freedom – being free and independent

fugitive – a person who is running away from something

plantation – a large area of land where certain crops are grown, e.g., sugar, tea

slave – a person who is owned by another person and works without being paid